Debbie Eason

ESSENTIALS

GCSE Design & Technology
Graphic Products
Workbook

Contents

Communication Techniques

Presentation Drawings

Design & Market Influences

Contents

Communication Techniques

Sketching and Tools

1 Choose the correct words from the options given to complete the following sentences.

| **pencils** | **three dimensions** | **straight** | **shape** | **rendering** | **light** |

a) Freehand sketching is a quick method that uses ___pencils___ and / or pens to create

some design ideas and accentuate ___shape___ and form. Crating enables you to draw

in ___three dimensions___, using ___straight___ lines.

b) You can create tone by shading to show areas of ___light___ and dark. This process is

called ___rendering___.

2 Which of the following tools are suitable for sketching? Tick the correct options.

A Templates ◯   **B** Coloured pencils ✓

C Scale ruler ◯   **D** Marker pens ✓

E Graphite pencils ✓

3 Circle the correct option in the following sentence.

When rendering a shiny surface, you are reproducing the **texture** / **crating** for plastic or glass.

4 The table contains the names of three elements of drawing.

Match descriptions **A**, **B** and **C** with the elements **1–3** in the table.
Enter the appropriate number in the boxes provided.

	Element
1	Watercolours
2	Pastels
3	Texture

A Creates an illusion of a surface effect   3

B Makes a good background when sketching   1

C Needs to be 'fixed' after sketching with them   2

5 What source do you need to show when creating dark and light tones on your drawing?

_____

Colour

Primary and Secondary Colours AQA • OCR

1 Circle the correct option in the following sentences.

a) **Primary** / **Secondary** colours are created by mixing colours together.

b) There are **three** / **four** primary colours.

2 Which of the following are primary colours? Tick the correct options.

A Green ☐   B Yellow ☑

C Red ☑   D Orange ☐

E Purple ☐   F Blue ☑

Complementary Colours AQA • OCR

3 Which of the following are complementary colours? Tick the correct options.

A Red and green ☑   B Purple and yellow ☑

C Red and blue ☐   D Yellow and orange ☐

E Blue and orange ☑   F Green and yellow ☐

Hue and Tone AQA • OCR

4 How would you lighten the tone of a colour?

Add some white

Colour Fusion and Separation

5 Fill in the missing words to complete the following sentence.

Colour separation happens in printing where layers of cyan, Magenta,
Yellow and Black are overlaid.

6 What is colour fusion?

Where you mix colours together to make another colour

Colour

1 The table contains three colours.

Match the meanings **A, B** and **C** with the colours **1–3** in the table.
Enter the appropriate number in the boxes provided.

	Colours
1	Blue
2	Yellow
3	Red

A Anger and danger `3`

B Sunshine and happiness `2`

C Natural and calming `1`

2 Which of the following describe the colour orange? Tick the correct options.

A Vibrant and warm `✓`   **B** Citrus fruit colour `✓`

C Represents envy ☐   **D** Represents balance and harmony ☐

E Represents lavender ☐

3 Which of the following describe the colour purple? Tick the correct options.

A Represents growth ☐   **B** Represents royalty `✓`

C Represents good health `✓`   **D** Boosts creativity ☐

E Represents the environment ☐

4 Fill in the missing words to complete the following sentences.

a) Colours can be used to indicate certain categories of _____. White and blue

denote _____. Green and brown denote _____ products.

b) Colours are used in different _____ and religions to represent or symbolise

something. Be careful not to use colours in your design that might _____ someone.

☐

Logos and Trademarks · AQA • OCR

1 Give an example of a well known logo.

Nike ✓

2 The table contains four symbols.

Match the descriptions **A, B, C** and **D** with the symbols **1–4** in the table. Enter the appropriate number in the boxes provided.

	Symbols
1	**TM**
2	**SM**
3	©
4	®

A Put against a company name to prevent other companies from copying their product or service 3

B Used when a company delivers a service and is waiting for their registration to go through 2

C Registered to the company 4

D A word, phrase, symbol or design, which identifies and distinguishes the goods of one company 1

Corporate Identity and Brand Names

3 Explain what a brand name is.

4 Give an example of a brand name that tells the customer what the product is all about.

Typography

1 Are the following sentences **true** or **false**?

a) Sans serifs are strokes that finish off the end of stems. _False_

b) Small letters are also known as uppercase letters. _False_

c) A font is a specific typeface of a certain size and style. _True_

d) Typography is lettering used to create an effect. _True_

2 Which of the following are styles of serif lettering? Tick the correct options.

A Hairline ○

B Justified ○

C Slab ○

D Integral ○

E Full bracketed ○

3 The table contains three terms associated with typography.

Match descriptions **A, B** and **C** with the terms **1–3** in the table. Enter the appropriate number in the boxes provided.

	Terms
1	Serifs
2	Lower case
3	Font

A Small letters _2_

B Typeface _3_

C Strokes on the end of stems _1_

4 Explain the difference between a sans serif typeface and a serif typeface.

Sans-serif is where the text is normal and doesn't have any fancy flicks at the start or ends of a letter, wheras serif is where it does have the fancy flicks.

Letter Spacing

1 Choose the correct words from the options given to complete the following sentences.

width   **kerning**   **text**   **tracking**   **spacing**

The ease at which you can read _text_ depends upon the _Spacing_

between the letters. _Tracking_ is where the letters are adjusted in pairs and

Kerning is where all the letters are increased or decreased in _Width_

to make the word(s) more evenly spaced.

2 The table contains the names of three types of spacing that can be used for text.

Match descriptions **A, B**, and **C** with the words **1–3** in the table. Enter the appropriate number in the boxes provided.

	Spacing
1	Justified
2	Kerning
3	Tracking

A   Lettering that is adjusted in pairs ⬡ 3

B   The size of the lettering is made smaller or larger to evenly space them ⬡ 2

C   The alignment of text where the text sits flush with the left and right hand margins ⬡ 1

Text Alignment and Word Spacing

3 Give four types of text alignment used on your computer.

a) _Centered_

b) _Left alignment_

c) _Right alignment_

d) _Evenly fitted_

4 Fill in the missing words to complete the following sentences.

a) _____ is the space between words.

b) The small letter _____ is normally used between small letters to divide words.

c) The large letter _____ is used for spacing between upper case letters

to divide words.

Drawing Techniques and Materials

Grids and Tracing Paper

1 List four types of grid.

a) Letter grids   b) isometric grid   c) perspective grid   d) Number grid

2 Choose the correct words from the options given to complete the following sentences.

working drawings   **grid**   **image**   **tracing**   **copied**

You could use a ___grid___ sheet behind tracing paper to help you draw accurately.

A(n) ___image___ from a magazine can be ___copied___ onto

___tracing___ paper and then transferred onto your paper.

___working___   ___drawings___ can be done on tracing paper too.

3 Which of the following methods are suitable for copying images? Tick the correct options.

A Paper ☐   **B** Tracing paper ☑

C Working drawings ☑   **D** Marker pens ☐

E Scanning ☑

4 The table contains three drawing techniques / materials.

Match descriptions **A**, **B** and **C** with the techniques / materials **1–3** in the table. Enter the appropriate number in the boxes provided.

A Comes in mm and inches and is used for measuring drawings ③

B Can be drawn on tracing paper ①

C Comes in line or dot format and can be used to draw angles correctly ②

	Technique / Material
1	Working drawing
2	Isometric grid
3	Square grid

Paper and Board Measurements

5 Circle the correct options in the following sentences.

a) Paper comes in different sizes and **depths** / **weights** for different functions. Paper over **100** / **200**g/m² is classed as **board** / **corrugated cardboard**.

b) A4 paper measures **210 x 297mm** / **420 x 594mm**. 2 x A4 sheets is the same size as 1 x **A5** / **A3** sheet.

Drawing Techniques and Materials

Types of Paper and Board

Revision Guide Reference: Page 11

1 Choose the correct words from the options given to complete the following sentences.

fluted **transparent** **visualising** **bleached** **layers** **printing** **corrugated**

White board is a strong material whose surface has been _Bleached_ to provide an

excellent surface for _printing_ . Layout paper is a thin, fairly _transparent_

paper, which provides a cheap medium for designers to use for _visualising_ a design.

Corrugated card has two _Layers_ with a _fluted_ inner section.

2 Which of the following describe corrugated cardboard? Tick the correct options.

A Supplies protection during transportation ◯

B Transparent ◯

D Recyclable ◯

E Fluted inner section ✓

F Bleached surface ◯

3 The table contains the names of three materials.

Match descriptions **A**, **B** and **C** with the materials **1–3** in the table. Enter the appropriate number in the boxes provided.

	Material
1	Layout paper
2	Grey board
3	Cartridge paper

A Soft surface used with crayons, pastels, inks, watercolours and gouache ③

B Thin, fairly transparent white paper used by designers ①

C Use in schools for model-making ②

4 Are the following statements **true** or **false**?

a) White board is cheap and used for visualisation purposes. _False_

b) Cardboard is cheap and recyclable. _True_

c) Duplex board is used mainly in food packaging. _True_

d) Bleed-proof paper is used for protection of goods for packaging. _False_

Drawing Tools

Equipment and Templates

1 Name three templates used for drawing shapes and specify what shapes they can help you draw.

a) ....

b) ....

c) ....

2 a) Choose the correct words from the options given to complete the following sentences.

scale   parallel   protractor   measurements

i) A _protractor_ is used for measuring angles.

ii) A _Scale_ ruler has different scales worked out for you, so you spend less

time working out _mesurements_ to fit the page.

iii) A drawing board has a _parallel_ motion.

b) What three angles would you use with set squares?

....

3 Complete the following table to show the functions of the equipment.

Equipment	Function
Set square	
French curve	
Circle template	

4 Circle the correct options in the following sentences.

a) A set square comes in different angles and is used to help with **oblique / isometric** drawings. You can also use a set square for a **45 / 65** degree angle for work on orthographic projections.

b) French curves are used to draw **angles / arcs. Flexi / French** curves can be adjusted to any arc you need.

Pencils and Pens

1 The following table contains the names of drawing tools and their functions. Complete the table.

Tools	Function
Fineline black technical pen	Used for sketching and outlines
Graphite 2H and 6H pencil	
Marker pens	
	More accurate than a graphite pencil and used for construction lines.

2 a) What is the most commonly used size of fineline black technical pen?

0.5

b) List three other sizes that are commonly used.

i) 0.3 **ii)** 0.7 **iii)**

3 Name two advantages of using fibre-tipped pens for drawing.

a)

b)

4 Choose the correct words from the options given to complete the following sentences.
Any of the words can be used more than once.

outlines   **construction lines**   **shading and outlining**   **shading and toning**   **sketching**

a) Fineline black technical pens are useful for _____ or drawing _____ .

b) Fibre-tipped pens are good for _____ design ideas, but also for

_____ .

c) 2H and 6H graphite pencils are used for _____ .

d) Coloured pencils are used for _____ .

e) 2B and HB graphite pencils are used for _____ .

Plan Drawings

Scale

1 Complete the table about scales.

Description	Scale
Half the size of the actual object.	
Twice the size of the actual object.	

Scale Representations and Plans

2 Are the following statements **true** or **false**?

a) Exhibition and interior designers produce drawings in more detail than architects. ....

b) Interior designers design the building structure. ....

3 Draw lines between the boxes to match each designer with the product they may design.

Graphics designer	Displays
Exhibition designer	Pencil sharpener
Architect	Furniture
Interior designer	Logos
Product designer	Buildings

4 a) Choose the correct words from the options given to complete the following sentences.

scale   **architect**   **working drawings**   **plan**   **symbols**

.... are produced by designers in industry. Architects use

.... representations of household items in .... view. These

.... are used by a(n) ...., exhibition or interior designer.

b) Give the meanings of the following scale representations.

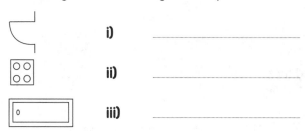

i) ....

ii) ....

iii) ....

Plan Drawings

Planometric Technique

1 Choose the correct words from the options given to complete the following sentences.

interior **height** **plan view** **3D** **45°/45°**

A planometric technique is used to give a .... impression of a product or

.... You can draw a .... and then tilt it to either a

.... or a 60°/30° angle. The .... will be reduced to $^3/_4$ of the

size, or it will look too tall.

Methods of Enlarging

2 Name three ways of enlarging images.

a) ....

b) ....

c) ....

Recognising Different Shapes

3 The table contains the number of sides of the shapes **A–C**.
Match the number of sides with the shapes.

A Rhombus ⬭

B Circle ⬭

C Triangle ⬭

	Number of Sides
1	1 sided
2	3 sided
3	4 sided

4 Are the following statements **true** or **false**?

a) A triangle is one of the weakest structural shapes. ....

b) A trapezium is a quadrilateral shape. ....

c) An ellipse template helps you to draw ellipses in isometric. ....

Isometric Projection

Isometric Projection

1 Which of the following explain what an isometric projection is? Tick the correct options.

    A It has one vanishing point   ◯

    B It is accurate and drawn to scale   ◯

    C It is drawn in 2D   ◯

    D It uses 30/60 degree angles   ◯

    E It is quicker than perspective drawing   ◯

2 The table contains the names of three types of drawing techniques.

Match descriptions **A, B** and **C** with the techniques **1–3** in the table.
Enter the appropriate number in the boxes provided.

	Drawing Techniques
1	Isometric projection
2	Exploded isometric
3	Perspective

    A Uses construction lines to show components of a drawing   ◯

    B Sketches a more realistic view using vanishing points   ◯

    C A 3D sketch technique using accurate dimensions   ◯

3 Are the following statements **true** or **false**?

    a) You can use ProDesktop to draw 3D views of an object.   ....

    b) Isometric can be drawn onto a grid sheet.   ....

    c) You need to draw a circle to help plot an ellipse in isometric.   ....

    d) Exploded drawings are quicker than drawing in perspective.   ....

    e) You use 30/60 degree angles to help draw a perspective.   ....

    f) Exploded drawings are not very accurate.   ....

    g) Exploded drawings are drawn to scale.   ....

Perspective Drawings

Perspective

1 The table contains elements of perspective drawing.

Match descriptions **A, B, C** and **D** with the elements **1–4** in the table.
Enter the appropriate number in the boxes provided.

	Elements
1	Vanishing point
2	Two point perspective
3	One point perspective
4	Horizon line

A All construction lines go to this.

B A point at which the sky meets the ground.

C Points sitting on the horizon line in opposite directions.

D All lines go to a point on the horizon line.

2 What is the horizon line also known as? Tick the correct option.

A A construction line

B A height line

C A dimension line

D An eye line

3 What are the advantages of using one point perspective? Tick the correct options.

A It can be used as an exploded view

B It can represent interiors in proportion

C You can read all measurements from every part of the drawing

D You can use it as a quick sketching method

4 Circle the correct option in the following sentences.

a) **One / Two** point perspective drawings are more commonly used to show an interior.

b) A(n) **horizon / construction** line has perspective points sitting on it.

c) **Two / Three** point perspective is where one point is sitting below the horizon line.

Perspective Drawings

Perspective (cont.)

1 Choose the correct words from the options given to complete the following sentences.

| one point | two point | above | horizon line | isometric |

A .... perspective gives a more realistic view than a ....

perspective. All perspective points sit on the .... where there are three positions for

the object to be: below, at or .... the line. Ellipses are plotted in a similar method to

the way you draw them in ....

2 Which of the following words are used in connection with perspective drawings? Tick the correct options.

A Workplanes ◯

B Construction lines ◯

C Assembly instructions ◯

D Specification for materials ◯

E ProDesktop ◯

3 Circle the correct options in the following sentence.

The **elevations / workplanes** are the surfaces you are working on and this term is used on the drawing software **ProDesktop / Publisher.**

4 The table contains the three elements of manufacturing drawings.

Match descriptions **A**, **B** and **C** with the elements **1–3** in the table. Enter the appropriate number in the boxes provided.

	Element
1	Proportion
2	Two point perspective
3	ProDesktop

A Uses workplanes to draw on the surface of an object ◯

B Represents a realistic view of an object ◯

C Relating to the height and depth of an object ◯

Standards in Working Drawings

Working Drawings

1 What should be included on working drawings in order for a prototype to be built? Tick the correct options.

- **A** Accurate measurements ◯
- **B** Price ◯
- **C** Assembly instructions ◯
- **D** Specification for materials ◯
- **E** Specification for finishes ◯

Standards

2 Are the following statements **true** or **false** regarding BSI standards on working drawings?

a) Always use centimetres for all the measurements. ....

b) Dimensions should be written above the dimension line. ....

c) Numbers can be written anywhere on the drawing. ....

d) Vertical dimensions are written to the left of a dimension line. ....

3 The table contains information on standards for working drawings.

Fill in the missing sections **A** to **D** in the spaces below.

Line	Name	Function
——————————	A	For dimension lines
██████████████	Continuous thick line	B
– · – · – · – · – · –	C	D

A ....

B ....

C ....

D ....

Standards in Working Drawings

Standards (cont.)

1 What do the following abbreviations stand for?

BS ....

....

EN ....

....

ISO...

....

2 The table contains names relating to standards in industry.

Match descriptions **A**, **B** and **C** with the standards **1–3** in the table.
Enter the appropriate number in the boxes provided.

	Standards
1	BS8888
2	Kitemark
3	BSI

A A voluntary certification scheme $\bigcirc$

B The organisation that sets standards of good working practice $\bigcirc$

C Standards set on working drawings $\bigcirc$

3 Choose the correct words from the options given to complete the following sentences.

integrity   **Kitemarks**   **quality**

.... are symbols of trust, ... and quality. They reassure

customers that the products they buy are thoroughly tested for ....

Copyright and Patents

4 Circle the correct options in the following sentences.

a) A **patent / standard** protects the company from other companies copying their new design or idea.

b) A **registered / logo** symbol can be put next to the company name to show that they have copyright protection.

Third Angle Orthographic Projection

1 Which of the following words are used in connection with 3rd angle orthographic drawing? Tick the correct options.

A Front view ◯

B Plan view ◯

C Inside view ◯

D Side view ◯

E Bird's eye view ◯

2 Fill in the missing words to complete the following sentences.

a) CAD stands for Computer ....

b) 3rd Angle .... shows up to four views of an object.

c) An orthographic generally shows plan view, side elevations and ....

....

d) An orthographic is used to produce your final idea so it can be made into a ....

3 Are the following statements **true** or **false**?

a) The front elevation is always on the left of the plan. ....

b) The plan is always at the top and above the front view. ....

c) There can be more than one side view on a drawing. ....

d) The plan view is drawn first so all elevations can be projected off them. ....

e) You leave in the construction lines on an orthographic projection. ....

4 What is the advantage of using CAD to draw third angle orthographic projections?

....

....

◯

Design and Market Influences

1 Which of the following explain what Harry Beck is famous for? Tick the correct options.

A   Corporate identity   ◯

B   Design of road signs   ◯

C   Design of coloured coded system for the underground   ◯

D   Enlisting famous artists and architects   ◯

E   Production of a schematic map   ◯

2 Choose the correct words from the options given to complete the following sentences.

1970   **Alessi**   **artists and architects**   **1921**

The _____ factory was founded by Alberto's grandfather in _____ .

Alberto took over the factory in _____ and enlisted _____ who helped to produce general homeware items.

3 The table contains the names of designers who have influenced the market today.

Match the names **1** and **2** in the table, to the facts **A–E**. Enter the appropriate number in the boxes provided.

A   Born in 1903; Died in 1974   ◯

B   Homeware items   ◯

C   Born 1946   ◯

D   Schematic map   ◯

E   Architects' and artists' work   ◯

	Names
1	Harry Beck
2	Alberto Alessi

4 Are the following statements **true** or **false**?

a) Harry Beck was famous for corporate identity and branding. _____

b) Alberto Alessi specialised in pop-up mechanisms. _____

c) Beck's design did not receive official recognition until the 1990s. _____

Influential Designs (cont.)   AQA

1 Are the following statements **true** or **false**?

a) Kinneir and Calvert designed signs for schools.   ....

b) Sabuda specialised in pop-up mechanisms in books.   ....

c) Sabuda was born in 1930.   ....

d) Wally Olins was famous for corporate identity and branding.   ....

e) Wally Olins produced logos for BT, Prudential and Volkswagen.   ....

f) Sabuda helped produce the pop-up version of the book

   Chronicles of Narnia.   ....

2 The table contains a list of designers.

Match descriptions **A**, **B**, and **C** with the designers **1–2** in the table. Enter the appropriate number in the boxes provided.

A Initially worked as a package designer   ◯

B Co-founded a company until 1997   ◯

C Gained recognition for this specialism in 1994   ◯

	Designers
1	Wally Olins
2	Robert Sabuda

3 Which of the following information matches with Kinneir and Calvert? Tick the correct options.

A Kinneir was born in 1918   ◯

B They designed a new signage system   ◯

C Their designs are still used today   ◯

D They designed the highway code   ◯

4 Fill in the missing words to complete the following sentences.

a) Wally Olins is one of the biggest practitioners of .... identity and

   ....

b) Robert Sabuda illustrated his first children's books in ....

Design and Market Influences

Ergonomics and Anthropometrics

1 Choose the correct words from the options given to complete the following sentences.

easier   **designers**   **humans**   **scientific**

Ergonomics is an application of .... information concerning

.... and their environment. .... always look at ergonomics,

with a view to making things .... to use.

2 The diagram shows somebody in the sitting position. Match descriptions **A–G** with the numbers **1–7** on the diagram. Enter the appropriate number in the boxes provided.

A   Sitting elbow height   ◯   **B**   Elbow–grip length   ◯

C   Buttock–knee length   ◯   **D**   Sitting height   ◯

E   Sitting eye height   ◯   **F**   Popliteal height   ◯

G   Buttock–popliteal length   ◯

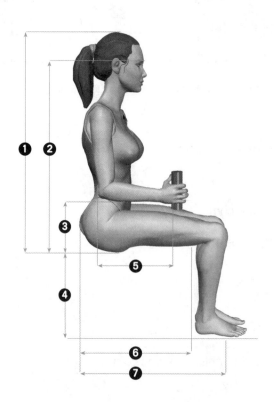

Design and Market Influences

Design Factors

1 Which of the following words are used in connection with ergonomic factors? Tick the correct options.

A Smell ◯

B Lines ◯

C Noise ◯

D Decoration ◯

E Weight ◯

F Size ◯

G Shape ◯

H Temperature ◯

Graphics

2 Circle the correct options in the following sentences.

a) It's important to choose a font where **style / boldness** is easy to read.

b) Contrast means that one **colour / tone** can stand out from another.

3 The table contains three terms that are important for ergonomics.

Match definitions **A**, **B** and **C** with the terms **1–3** in the table.
Enter the appropriate number in the boxes provided.

	Terms
1	Legibility
2	Contrast
3	Style

A A fashion or technique suitable for lettering or logos ◯

B A logo or lettering that is easy to read ◯

C When one colour stands out from another ◯

4 What condition does a person have if they can't distinguish certain colours from one another?

◻

Product Analysis

1 Are the following statements **true** or **false**?

a) The function of a product is when you look at your target market. ....

b) Product analysis is when you disassemble a product and evaluate it. ....

c) Built-in obsolescence isn't beneficial to the manufacturer. ....

d) When analysing a product, questionnaires are good for recording results. ....

2 Name three functions of milk.

a) ....

b) ....

c) ....

3 The table contains three product analysis categories.

Match definitions **A**, **B** and **C** with the analysis categories **1–3** in the table. Enter the appropriate number in the boxes provided.

A Who uses this product? ◯

B To demonstrate its purpose or how it is used ◯

C How much it is to manufacture and to dispose of after the products have been used ◯

Analysis Categories	
1	Function
2	Cost
3	Target Market

4 Choose the correct words from the options given to complete the following sentences.

obsolescence	**purpose**	**disassemble**	**analysis**	**made**

Product .... is when you .... a product and work out how it

is .... When you analyse the function of the product, you are looking at the

.... and the need for this particular object. You need to be aware of built-in

.... , which is the process of a product breaking down after a period of use.

Product Analysis (cont.)

1 Choose the correct words from the options given to complete the following sentences.

evaluate   **dates**   **originates**   **competitive**

When you analyse a product, you need to consider where it _____ from. When

looking at the history of a product, you need to look at events and _____, which may

be significant to how it evolved. _____ your product against a similar or

_____ product.

2 The table contains two milk containers.

Match the sentences **A–F** with the correct container labelled **1** or **2**. Enter the appropriate number in the boxes provided.

A   Difficult to reseal

B   Packaging is difficult to open

C   Bulky in transportation

D   Can be reused for other purposes

E   Can be easily thrown away with the household rubbish

F   Easy to open and reseal

	Milk Container
1	Milk carton
2	Plastic milk container

3 Name four things that you can compare, when you're evaluating your product against a similar or competitive product.

a) _____

b) _____

c) _____

d) _____

4 Why is hygiene an important factor in product analysis?

_____

_____

5 What is the name of the body, which has been set up to promote social and environmental fair trade?

_____

_____

Product Analysis

1 Which of the following are ergonomic factors associated with the design of a plastic milk container? Tick the correct options.

    A Cost ◯

    B Size of hand grips ◯

    C Manufacturing process ◯

    D Weight of the bottle when full ◯

    E Type of materials used ◯

2 Draw lines between the boxes to match each method of production with the correct example.

Method of Production		Example
Continuous mass production		Prototype for a board game
One-off production		Milk container

3 The table contains two types of manufacturing processes.

Match the descriptions **A–B** with the correct manufacturing process **1–2**.
Enter the appropriate number in the boxes provided.

    A Large scale ◯

    B Single product produced ◯

	Manufacturing Process
1	Batch production
2	One-off production

4 Fill in the missing words to complete the following sentences.

a) The cost of a product being made depends on whether it is mass / batch produced or a

    _____ production.

b) When analysing a product you should examine the origins and _____ of the

    material used.

The 6 'R's in Recycling

1 Choose the correct words from the options given to complete the following sentences.

> **environment**   **maintained**   **resources**   **society's**   **natural**

Sustainability is about redesigning the ways in which .... needs and wants are

met, without depleting .... or harming .... cycles for future

generations. These need to be .... to preserve the ....

2 List the six 'R's in recycling.

a) ....   **b)** ....   **c)** ....

d) ....   **e)** ....   **f)** ....

3 Which of the following things would you do to reuse a product? Tick the correct options.

   A Buy a single-use product

   B Throw your old product away in the general rubbish bin

   C Donate items

   D Get a product repaired

   E Sell items at a car boot sale

4 Which of the following explains what a designer would do when designing sustainable products? Tick the correct options.

   A Create modern designs

   B Change existing designs

   C Design cheap products that can be thrown away

   D Consider using up existing resources

5 Fill in the missing words to complete the following sentences.

a) When you recycle products, it reduces the amount of material going to ....

.... This also reduces the necessity for mining and ....

down trees.

b) When you reduce waste, you use fewer .... to produce a product.

The Environment

Product Design and the Environment

1 Explain what Eco-design is.

_____

2 What does biodegradable mean? Tick the correct option.

A Products that do not grow naturally in the environment ⬭

B Products that are broken down naturally in the environment ⬭

C Products that are reusable ⬭

D Products that can't be decomposed ⬭

3 The table contains types of materials.

Match the words **A–I** with the two terms labelled **1** and **2** to show which products are biodegradable and which are non-biodegradable. Enter the appropriate number in the boxes provided.

A Apples ⬭   **B** Tin can ⬭

C Plants ⬭   **D** Glass ⬭

E Plastic packaging ⬭   **F** Cardboard ⬭

G Cotton clothes ⬭   **H** Banana ⬭

I Aluminium ⬭

	Types of Materials
1	Biodegradable
2	Non-biodegradable

4 Explain what a 'landfill site' is.

_____

The Ecological Footprint

5 Choose the correct words from the options given to complete the following sentences.

demands   **ecological**   **human**   **carbon**   **natural**

The _____ footprint (also known as the _____ footprint) is the

_____ demand on the Earth's _____ resources and the Earth's

ability to keep up with the _____ humans put on it.

Energy Sources

Edexcel

1 Complete the table below to identify the renewable types of energy and their sources.

Type of Renewable Energy	Energy Source
a)	Wind
Solar cells and panels	**b)** ....
c)	Organic matter

2 Name the three categories of silicon cells.

a) ....

b) ....

c) ....

3 Are the following statements **true** or **false**?

a) Fossil fuels are non-renewable energy sources. ....

b) Solar cells capture electricity and turn it into heat. ....

c) Water power drives turbines that generate electricity. ....

d) Coal is a renewable energy source. ....

e) Non-renewable energy sources will eventually run out. ....

f) Oil and gas are continually available. ....

4 What is the Kyoto Protocol?

....

....

....

Modelling

Materials for Modelling

1 Which of the following statements describe corrugated plastic sheet? Tick the correct options.

    A   Creates sculptural shapes in layers   ◯

    B   Has two sheets with a fluted centre   ◯

    C   Can be paint finished with emulsion   ◯

    D   Used in high quality packaging   ◯

    E   A very absorbent material   ◯

    F   Not suitable for moulding   ◯

2 The table contains the names of four materials that can be used for modelling.

Match descriptions **A, B, C** and **D** with the materials **1–4** in the table. Enter the appropriate number in the boxes provided.

	Material
1	Styrofoam™
2	Hard wax
3	MDF
4	Plaster bandage

    A   Manufactured fibreboard, with no grain   ◯

    B   A material that is used wet onto a wire mesh or other surface   ◯

    C   A material that is melted down and reformed into a mould   ◯

    D   A dense version of polystyrene that can be cut, moulded and joined easily   ◯

3 Which material is often used in architectural modelling? Tick the correct option.

    A   MDF   ◯

    B   Acrylic   ◯

    C   Corrugated plastic   ◯

    D   Foam board   ◯

4 Circle the correct option in the following sentence.

Acrylic is a very **brittle / soft** material that is difficult to **join / mould** together.

Adhesives for Model Making

1 Choose the correct words from the options given to complete the following sentences.

| Unibond™ | colourless | wood | polyvinyl acetate | adhesive |

.... is sometimes also called Resin W™ or ...., which bonds

.... or card. PVA is a white .... that dries

.... and sets in three hours.

2 List two adhesives you could use to stick paper to paper.

a) ....

b) ....

3 Which of the following adhesives need a well-ventilated room in order to be safe to use? Tick the correct options.

A Glue stick ◯   **B** Aerosol ◯

C PVA ◯   **D** Balsa cement ◯

E Acrylic cement ◯

4 Circle the correct option in the following sentence.

Acrylic cement **sticks / welds** plastic together.

5 The table contains the names of three types of adhesives.

Match descriptions **A**, **B** and **C** with the adhesives **1–3** in the table. Enter the appropriate number in the boxes provided.

	Adhesives
1	Epoxy resin
2	Rubber-based cement
3	Glue guns

A The glue is heated up electronically and cools quickly on contact. ◯

B A two-part adhesive, which creates a strong bond in 4–5 minutes. ◯

C Applied to two surfaces, then a 10-minute wait is needed before the surfaces are brought together. ◯

Modelling

Fixatives and Masking

1 The table contains the names of three masking techniques.

Match descriptions **A**, **B** and **C** with the masking techniques **1–3** in the table. Enter the appropriate number in the boxes provided.

	Masking Techniques
1	Sheet
2	Fluid
3	Tape

A Self-adhesive and you can use a scalpel to cut out shapes ◯

B Used to stick onto paper to mask off small areas ◯

C Applied to very intricate areas, allowed to dry, then peeled off ◯

2 Circle the correct options in the following sentences.

a) A fixative is used to fix **soft pencils / ink pen** to card or paper.

b) To fix materials together you can also use **fillers / velcro®**.

Tools

3 The table contains the names of four tools that can be used for modelling.

Match descriptions **A**, **B**, **C** and **D** with the tools **1–4** in the table. Enter the appropriate number in the boxes provided.

	Tools
1	Scroll saw
2	Creasing bar
3	Rotary cutter
4	Scalpel

A Has a blade that rotates and cuts straight lines or circles in thin card ◯

B A machine that creates creases in cardboard ◯

C Cuts wood and plastics into intricate shapes ◯

D Used with a safety ruler to cut cardboard ◯

Finishes

Edexcel • AQA

1 Choose the correct words from the options given to complete the following sentences.

| photograph | heat | pouch | encapsulation |

_____ is when a picture or a _____ is enclosed in a pocket or

_____ and then sealed with _____ .

2 Which of the following statements describe picture framing? Tick the correct options.

A Creates a background for pictures ⬭

B The mounting board is measured in height ⬭

C Cardboard mounts are also known as 'mounting board' ⬭

D Masking tape is used to attach the window to the picture ⬭

E Can be sanded down after putting in place ⬭

F A window is created in cardboard ⬭

3 What can be used to fill holes in your models?

_____

Paints and Inks

Edexcel • AQA

4 The table contains the names of three paint finishes that can be used for finishing your model.

Match descriptions **A**, **B**, and **C** with the paints **1–3** in the table. Enter the appropriate number in the boxes provided.

A Has not got a shiny surface ⬭

B Uses a medium of natural drying oil called linseed ⬭

C Has a slight shimmer to the finish ⬭

	Paint
1	Gloss
2	Satin
3	Matt

5 Circle the correct options in the following sentences.

a) Lacquers consist of a synthetic **plastic / resin** dissolved in an organic solvent.

b) Oil-based gloss is durable and **colourless / waterproof**.

Modelling

1 Which of the following describe emulsions? Tick the correct options.

    A Contains linseed oil   ◯

    B Waterproof   ◯

    C Water-based   ◯

    D Contain vinyl or acrylic resin   ◯

    E Not waterproof   ◯

2 What substance are the following statements referring to?

It comes in three types – water soluble, water resistant and solvent based.
It is most commonly used in printing, but not necessarily in model making.

---

3 The table contains the names of three pre-manufactured components that can be used for finishing your model.

Match descriptions **A**, **B** and **C** with the materials **1–3** in the table. Enter the appropriate number in the boxes provided.

	Pre-manufactured Components
1	Click fasteners
2	Eyelets
3	Paper fasteners

    A Used to attach two pieces of paper together to make a mechanical movement   ◯

    B Comprise two plastic rivets, which hold two pieces of card together   ◯

    C Fasten into sheet material to reinforce a hole   ◯

4 Which material is suitable for the production of eyelets? Tick the correct option.

    A Acrylic   ◯   **B** Lead   ◯

    C Brass   ◯   **D** Wood   ◯

1 The table contains the names of four pre-manufactured components that can be used for finishing your model.

Match descriptions **A, B, C** and **D** with the materials **1–4** in the table. Enter the appropriate number in the boxes provided.

	Pre-manufactured Components
1	Velcro®
2	Pressfit
3	Double-sided sticky pads
4	Double-sided tape

A   Works by friction, resulting in parts staying together ◯

B   Transparent and self-adhesive on both sides ◯

C   Has looped material on one side and hooks on the other ◯

D   Made of foam and self-adhesive on both sides ◯

2 Choose the correct words from the options given to complete the following sentences.

strengths   **bearings**   **tensile**   **connectors**   **friction**

Pressfit relies on _____ and compression _____ of the material to

'fit' together. Examples are metal _____ and water tight _____.

The pressfit works by the parts staying together with the use of _____.

3 Circle the correct option in the following sentences.

a)   Double-sided tape is **white / transparent** tape, which has self-adhesive on both surfaces.

b)   Double-sided sticky pads are made of **acrylic / foam** and are useful for sticking cardboard together.

4 Which of the following statements describes Velcro®? Tick the correct option.

A   It comprises two pieces of material that are self-adhesive ◯

B   It has loop fasteners on both pieces of material ◯

C   It has two looped surfaces that hold the Velcro® together ◯

D   It has hooked material on one side and looped material on the other ◯

Smart and Modern Materials

Smart & Modern Materials

1 a) Name three changes in the environment that can affect smart materials.

i) ....

ii) ....

iii) ....

b) What enables smart materials, under the right conditions, to return to their original state?

....

2 The table contains the names of two types of smart materials.

Match descriptions **A–D** with the smart materials **1–2** in the table. Enter the appropriate number in the boxes provided.

A Changes colour in response to changes in light intensity ◯

B Made of liquid crystals or metal compounds ◯

C Used for windows in coaches and cars ◯

D Used for T-shirts ◯

	Smart Material
1	Thermochromic
2	Photochromic

3 Choose the correct words from the options given to complete the following sentences.

dark	exposed	visible	afterglow	paint

A phosphorescent material is known as a(n) .... or glow in the

.... material. It produces .... or invisible light by absorbing

light when .... to a light source. It can be applied to materials as a

.... or spray form.

4 The table contains the names of three smart/modern materials.

Match descriptions **A, B** and **C** with the materials **1–3** in the table. Enter the appropriate number in the boxes provided.

A Used for disposable trays and plates ◯

B Used for TV screens ◯

C Thermoplastic that can be shaped and reshaped ◯

	Smart / Modern
1	Potatopak
2	Polymorph
3	LCD

Nanotechnology

1 What scale is nanotechnology dealing with? Tick the correct option.

A 1: 10 ◯

B Minute ◯

C Molecular ◯

D Minuscule ◯

E Miniature ◯

2 What can a nano-material be used for? Tick the correct options.

A Self-cleaning materials ◯

B Sports clothing ◯

C Lubricants ◯

D In paint as a colour ◯

E Food packaging ◯

3 Choose the correct words from the options given to complete the following sentences.

repels   **odours**   **Nanotechnology**   **protect**   **applications**   **garments**

_____ can produce clothing that _____ dirt, stains and body

_____ and can 'self-clean' with a cup of water. It can also produce

_____ that can sense, react and absorb an impact or collision and so

_____ your body. These can be used in extreme sports or military

_____ .

Carbon Fibres

4 Circle the correct options in the following sentences.

a) Carbon fibres can be **printed / woven** into a fabric sheet and then impregnated with an epoxy resin or phenolic resin.

b) The carbon fibre material is cured with heated steam to create a very **heavyweight / lightweight** material.

Types of Plastics

Plastics

1 (Circle) the correct options in the following sentences.

a) **Thermosetting plastics / Thermoplastics** will not soften when reheated

b) **Thermosetting plastics / Thermoplastics** will soften when reheated

2 Which of the following additives can be added to plastics to make the quality of the material different? Tick the correct options.

A Resin ◯   B Polyester ◯   C Pigments ◯

D Formaldehyde ◯   E Stabilisers ◯   F Anti-static agents ◯

3 Choose the correct words from the options given to complete the following sentences.

polymers   **monomers**   **polymerisation**   **manufactured**

Plastics can be used for a wide variety of products and are _____ using a process

known as _____ . This occurs when _____ join together to form

long chains of molecules called _____ .

Types of Plastics

4 Are the following statements about thermosetting plastics **true** or **false**?

a) Will soften if reheated as the polymers are interlinked _____

b) Can be recycled _____

c) Very soft and flexible plastic _____

d) Can be heated and moulded into shape _____

5 Are the following statements about thermoplastics **true** or **false**?

a) Can be recycled _____

b) Reinforced with glass fibre _____

c) Will soften when reheated and shaped when hot _____

d) Will harden when cooled, but can be reshaped if heated again _____

Types of Plastics (cont.)

1) The table contains the abbreviations of some plastics.

Match the different plastics **A–G** with the abbreviations **1–7** in the table. Enter the appropriate number in the boxes provided.

A Epoxy Resin ◯

B Polyester Resin ◯

C Polypropylene ◯

D Low Density Polyethylene ◯

E High Density Polyethylene ◯

F Polystyrene ◯

G Melamine Formaldehyde ◯

	Abbreviations for Plastics
1	HDPE
2	PR
3	ER
4	LDPE
5	PS
6	PP
7	MF

2) Which of the following statements describe Phenol Formaldehyde? Tick the correct options.

A It is a colourless polymer ◯

B It is a hard, brittle plastic ◯

C It is used for making nets and storage containers ◯

D It is a dark colour with a gloss finish ◯

E It is used for making electrical fittings ◯

3) The table contains the names of five different plastics.

Match the different uses **A–E** with the plastics **1–5** in the table. Enter the appropriate number in the boxes provided.

A Sound and heat insulation ◯

B Car bodies and boats ◯

C Printed circuit boards ◯

D Decorative worktops ◯

E Medical equipment ◯

	Plastics
1	Melamine Formaldehyde
2	Polyester resin
3	Polystyrene
4	Polypropylene
5	Epoxy Resin

4) Which type of plastic is available as a clear, matt or prepared film?

◯

Industrial Processes

1 Name three materials that are commonly used for injection moulding.

a) ....

b) ....

c) ....

2 Choose the correct words from the options given to complete the following sentences.

mould   **plastic**   **hopper**   **granules**   **cooled**   **hydraulic**

Plastic powder or .... are fed from the .... into a hollow

steel barrel. The heaters melt the .... as the screw moves it towards the

.... The .... system forces plastic into the mould, while

pressure is maintained until it has .... enough to be opened.

Extrusion

3 **a)** Label the following diagram for the extrusion process.

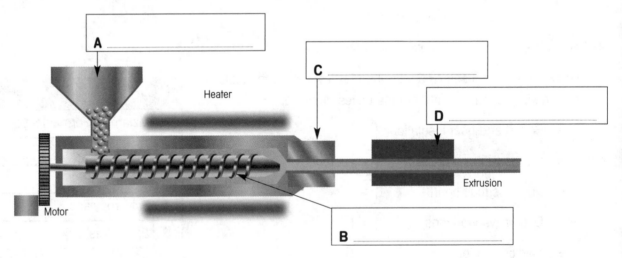

A ....

Heater

C ....

D ....

Extrusion

Motor

B ....

b) What is the purpose of **D**?

....

c) What is fed into **A**?

....

Industrial Processes

Blow Moulding

1 Name three common materials used in the blow moulding process.

a) ....

b) ....

c) ....

2 The following statements **A–E** are stages in the blow moulding process. Number them **1–5** to show the correct order.

A Air is blown into an extruded section of the tube.

B Air forces plastic to the sides of the mould.

C When it is cooled, the mould is opened and the product is removed.

D The air expands.

E Plastic granules are fed into a hopper by a rotating screw.

Compression Moulding

3 What type of press is used to create a shape in compression moulding? Tick the correct option.

A Mould

B Chamber

C Hydraulic

D Vacuum

4 Choose the correct words from the options given to complete the following sentences about compression moulding.

mould   polymer   thermosetting   powder   slug

A large force is used to squash a cube of .... into a heated

.... This cube of polymer is in the form of a .... known as a

.... Compression moulding is used with .... plastics.

Industrial Processes

Vacuum Forming

1 What is the reason for using polystyrene for vacuum forming?

_____

2 Are the following statements about the vacuum forming process **true** or **false**?

a) Acrylic sheets are often used for this process. ....

b) This process uses a laser beam to form shapes. ....

c) The most popular material to use is styrene. ....

d) Plastics are heated up and pressed onto a mould. ....

e) Removing air causes the hot plastic to be sucked onto the mould. ....

Line Bending

3 Explain how a line bending machine works.

_____

_____

_____

4 Label **A** and **B** on the following diagram.

A ....

B ....

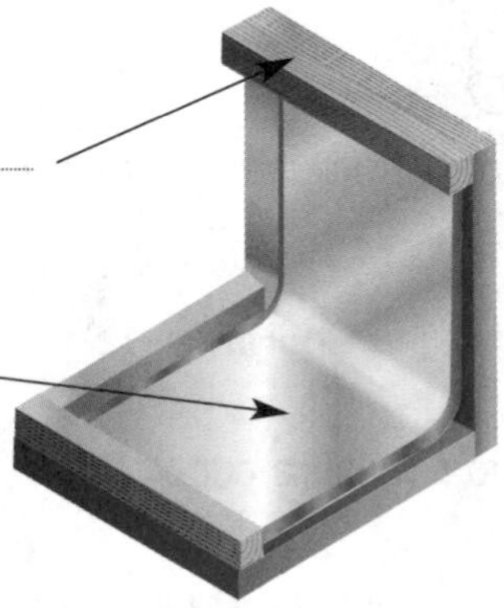

5 In line bending, what can you use to produce accurate angles and shapes after the acrylic has been heated? Tick the correct option.

A Vacuum former ⬭   **B** Mould ⬭

C Bending jig ⬭   **D** Polymer ⬭

Laser Cutting

1 Which of the following describe laser cutting? Tick the correct options.

A The laser activates a jig ◯

B A series of windows direct the light down onto the material ◯

C Used for cutting plastics ◯

D Used for cutting fabrics ◯

E The material absorbs the laser when exposed to a light source ◯

2 Choose the correct words from the options given to complete the following sentences.

heat   **polished**   **mirrors**   **optics**   **material**

A series of .... direct the laser beam vertically down onto the

.... to be cut. This is also known as flying .... As the laser

beam hits the material, the intense .... vapourises it, leaving a

.... surface.

3 What do motorised actuators do? Tick the correct options.

A Start up the laser cutting machine ◯   **B** Move the mirrors ◯

C Adjust the cutting position ◯   **D** Vapourise the material ◯

4 Name three sign-making materials that can be cut using lasers.

a) ....

b) ....

c) ....

5 Name four fabrics that can be cut using lasers.

a) ....

b) ....

c) ....

d) ....

Industrial Practice

Methods of Production

1 What is producing a one-off product also known as? Tick the correct option.

A A first product ⬭ **B** Single unit ⬭

C Prototype ⬭ **D** A cell ⬭

2 The table contains the names of six methods of production.

Match descriptions **A–F** with the methods of production **1–6** in the table. Enter the appropriate number in the boxes provided.

	Methods of Production
1	One-off
2	Cell
3	Just in time
4	Logistics
5	Mass
6	Batch

A Production of individual parts made independently ⬭

B The arrival of component parts at exactly the time that they are needed ⬭

C A production that involves a product being made on a very large scale ⬭

D When a single product is made ⬭

E A series of products made together in small or large quantities ⬭

F Ensuring that materials and resources are in the right place at the right time ⬭

3 What type of production method does a mobile phone or a car require? Tick the correct option.

A Logistics ⬭

B Batch production ⬭

C Cell production ⬭

D Continuous production ⬭

Printing Processes

Methods of Printing

1 What method of printing is shown in the following picture?
Tick the correct option.

A Flexography ◯

B Block printing ◯

C Letterpress ◯

D Lithography ◯

2 Is the following statement **true** or **false**?

Letterpress is generally used for cheap paper back books. ....

3 Choose the correct words from the options given to complete the following sentences.

roller   **paper**   **lino**   **transferred**   **surface**

Block printing is where the image is drawn onto ...., which is then cut away from

around the image, so the image sits proud from the .... Ink is applied, then the

.... is pressed onto the lino using a ...., so the image is

.... onto the paper.

4 Which of the following describe flexography? Tick the correct options.

A Metal letters have to be individually made ◯

B Uses flexible rubber or plastic plates for cylinders ◯

C The image is drawn onto lino ◯

D Used in short runs for stationery ◯

E Used for packaging ◯

5 Name four materials that can be printed on using flexography.

a) ....

b) ....

c) ....

d) .... ◯

Printing Processes

Gravure Printing

1 What is the disadvantage of gravure? Tick the correct option.

A It only makes a few copies at a time ◯

B It will only print in black and white ◯

C It is very expensive to set up ◯

D It is not a very high quality print finish ◯

2 How is the gravure plate made? Tick the correct option.

A From wood ◯   **B** From paper ◯

C Photographically ◯   **D** From a mesh ◯

Screen Printing

3 Match the descriptions **A–F** with the illustrations of the stages **1–6** for screen printing. Enter the appropriate number in the boxes provided.

1	2	3
4	5	6

A Ink is then squeezed through the nylon fabric mesh by using a rubber-bladed 'squeegee'. ◯

B The screen is then lowered and secured in position. ◯

C The ink then passes through the unblocked area of the stencil to produce your final printed image, when the screen is removed. ◯

D The screen is made as a wooden frame. Nylon fabric is cut 5cm larger than the frame and then stretched and stapled. ◯

E The shape is cut out of paper and either part is used to create the stencil. ◯

F The screen is hinged to allow it to be raised and lowered without it changing position. The stencil and your paper (or fabric) are placed under the screen. ◯

Planographic Printing

1 What is the most common form of planographic printing? Tick the correct option.

    A Relief printing ⬭

    B Screen printing ⬭

    C Gravure printing ⬭

    D Offset lithography ⬭

2 Circle the correct options in the following sentences.

    a) The abbreviation for the four-colour process in lithography is **MCYK** / **CMYK**.

    b) The order the colours go in are **cyan, magenta, yellow, black** / **cyan, yellow, black, magenta**.

3 **a)** Fill in the missing labels on this diagram of a single feed lithography process.

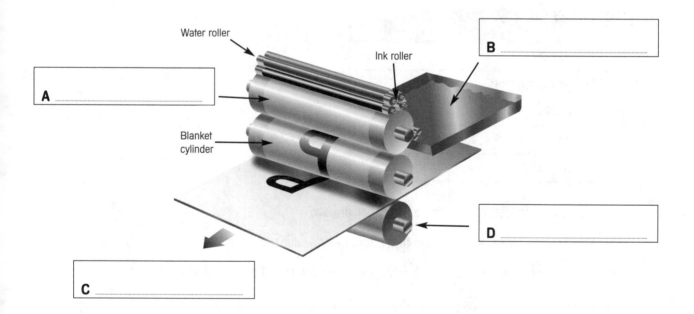

Water roller

Ink roller

B ....

A ....

Blanket cylinder

D ....

C ....

    b) Explain what the function of **B** is in the above diagram.

....

....

Printing Processes

Dry Printing

1 What is the name of the dry printing process used by photocopiers and laser printers? Tick the correct option.

A Xerography ⬭
B Flexography ⬭
C Gravure printing ⬭
D Lithography ⬭

2 In Computer Aided Design packages, what does WYSIWYG stand for and what does it mean?

_____

Finishes

3 The table contains the names of five printing finishes.

Match descriptions **A–E** with the printing finishes **1–5** in the table. Enter the appropriate number in the boxes provided.

	Printing Finishes
1	Lamination
2	Microencapsulation
3	Holographic
4	Embossing
5	UV Varnishing

A Raises or indents in the surface of paper or card ⬭

B When microcapsules burst, the tiny particles are released ⬭

C A high gloss clear liquid, which is applied over the top of a printed area ⬭

D A pattern that appears to have three dimensions ⬭

E Applying a clear protective film over the printed image ⬭

Book Binding Edexcel

4 Which method of book binding allows books to be taken apart and put together again by hand without the book being damaged? Tick the correct option.

A Saddle wire stitching ⬭
B Hard binding ⬭
C Perfect binding ⬭
D Comb binding ⬭

Planning Your Work

1 a) What is the following chart called?

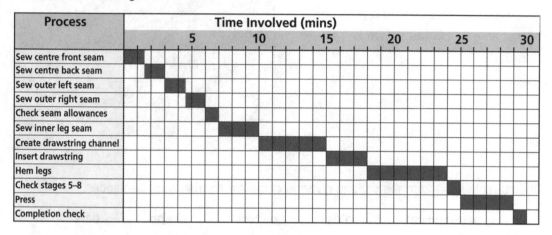

Process	Time Involved (mins)					
	5	10	15	20	25	30
Sew centre front seam						
Sew centre back seam						
Sew outer left seam						
Sew outer right seam						
Check seam allowances						
Sew inner leg seam						
Create drawstring channel						
Insert drawstring						
Hem legs						
Check stages 5–8						
Press						
Completion check						

....

b) What is the function of this chart?

....

....

2 What are the names of the following shaped boxes used in flow charts?

a) ....

b) ....

c) ....

d) ....

Plan of Manufacture

3 Why is a plan of manufacture used? Tick the correct options.

A To make design decisions

B Explains how a printing process works

C Provides details of resources needed to make your product

D Lists a sequence of tasks that need to be completed for the making of a product

E Lists the risk assessments for each task

Packaging and Mechanisms

Developments

1 a) What is it called when you try to fit as many of the same shapes onto one piece of material as possible (as shown in the diagram)?

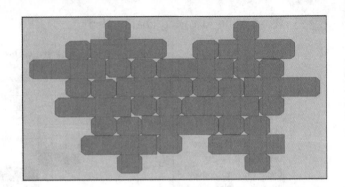

....

2 Choose the correct words from the options given to complete the following sentences.

development   **folds**   **cutters**   **shape**   **bars**

Die .... are used to press out the .... of the

...., while creasing .... are used to create the

.... in the development.

'Tuck In'

3 Add a label to the box to show the 'tuck in' tab.

Automatic Bases

4 What is an automatic base box? Tick the correct option.

A A box with a detachable base ◯

B A box that can be pushed open ◯

C A base that folds separately to the side panels ◯

D A base that has a slotted mechanism ◯

5 What does 'flat pack' mean and what is the advantage of a box being flat packed?

....

....

Packaging and Mechanisms

Functions of Packaging

1 Explain why food needs to be protected by its packaging.

_____

2 What are crates or cartons also known as? Tick the correct option.

A Containers ◯

B Inners ◯

C Boxes ◯

D Outers ◯

3 The table lists the functions of packaging.

Match the different properties of packaging **A–D** with the functions of packaging **1–4** in the table. Enter the appropriate number in the boxes provided.

A Packed to ensure products are sold hygienically ◯

B Used as a sales and marketing tool ◯

C Handled quickly and efficiently ◯

D Products arrive at their destination in one piece ◯

	Functions of Packaging
1	Transport
2	Protect
3	Promote
4	Preserve

4 Choose the correct words from the options given to complete the following sentences.

sell   **information**   **packaging**   **prevent**   **contents**   **damaged**

Labels provide _____ about a product. The label includes details like the

_____, weight and how it is used. Packaging can also be used to help

_____ and market a product. Food products are packed to _____

them from going rotten. The goods are protected from being _____, while in transit,

by their outer _____.

Packaging Materials

Paper and Board Packaging

1 Choose the correct words from the options given to complete the following sentences.

| absorb | foil | board | corrugated | lamination | transportation |

Paper and _____ can be used in conjunction with layers of thin

_____ and plastic together, to form a _____ . A board used for

packaging is called _____ cardboard. This is designed to _____

any impact during _____ .

2 Circle the correct option in the following sentences.

a) Thin layers of aluminium foil and plastic are called a **composite / lamination.**

b) **Foil / Plastic** retains heat, keeping food warm.

3 Are the following statements about paper and board packaging **true** or **false**?

a) Made from landfill waste

b) Board is thicker and heavier than paper

c) Made from wood pulp

d) Will harden when cooled, but can be reshaped if heated again

e) Board is good at absorbing shock

4 Which of the following items are foil laminated? Tick the correct options.

A Yoghurt carton lids ⬜   **B** Drink bottles ⬜

C Confectionary wrappers ⬜   **D** Leaflets ⬜

Advantages of Paper and Board

5 Which of the following are advantages of paper and board packaging? Tick the correct options.

A They can be laminated with foil for preservation ⬜   **B** Easy to store ⬜

C The materials are anti-static agents ⬜   **D** They can be recycled ⬜

E Materials are heavy ⬜   **F** Difficult to fold ⬜

Plastic Packaging

1 Which plastics are used to make bottle tops? Tick the correct options.

    A Polyester ⬭

    B Polypropylene ⬭

    C High density polyethylene ⬭

    D Polyvinyl chloride ⬭

2 Which of the following is made from polyester (PET)? Tick the correct option.

    A Bottle cap ⬭

    B Food tray ⬭

    C Fizzy drinks bottle ⬭

    D Book cover ⬭

    E Plastic carrier bag ⬭

3 The table contains the names of different plastics.

Match the different types of packaging **A–D** with the plastics **1–4** in the table.
Enter the appropriate number in the boxes provided.

	Plastics
1	Polyvinyl Chloride (PVC)
2	Polyester (PET)
3	Polystyrene (PS)
4	Polypropylene (PP)

    A Fizzy drink bottles ⬭

    B Tomato sauce bottle ⬭

    C Blister pack ⬭

    D Food tray ⬭

Packaging Materials

1 Give two advantages of using glass for commercial packaging.

a) ....

b) ....

Which Packaging to Use?

2 a) Name three products that are affected by light and oxygen.

i) .... **ii)** .... **iii)** ....

b) Name two products that are affected by moisture.

i) .... **ii)** ....

c) Name two drinks that can absorb smells and taste.

i) .... **ii)** ....

3 Fill in the gaps in the table using the words provided.

| Tinned food | Low density | Cereals | Drinks | Low cost | Coffee jars |
| Waterproof | Shatters | Expensive | Transparent | | |

Material	Advantages	Disadvantages	Uses for Packaging
Paper and Card	Low density **a)**	Affected by moisture and water	Toys **g)** .... Washing powders
Plastic (theromoplastic)	**b)** .... Waterproof Can be reheated	Affected by heat	**h)** .... Shampoos
Metal, e.g. steel and aluminium	Strong **c)**	**e)** .... High density	**i)** .... Fizzy drinks
Glass	Waterproof **d)**	**f)** .... Expensive High density	More expensive drinks **j)** ....

Types of Movement

Types of Movement — AQA • OCR

1 Match the types of movement **1–4** with the diagrams **A–D**. Enter the appropriate number in the spaces provided.

1 Reciprocating

2 Linear

3 Oscillating

4 Rotating

A _____ B _____ C _____ D _____

2 Choose the correct words from the options given to complete the following sentences.

oscillating　**direction**　**forwards**　**swings**　**movement**　**reciprocating**

A mechanism creates _____ within a product. A linear motion moves in one

_____, while a _____ motion moves backwards and

_____. A clock has a(n) _____ movement, which

_____ in alternate directions.

Levers – Basic Principles — AQA • OCR

3 The table contains the parts of levers.

Match descriptions **A**, **B**, and **C** with the terms **1–3** in the table. Enter the appropriate number in the boxes provided.

A When a force is applied

B The pivot point

C The resistance

	Terms
1	Fulcrum
2	Effort
3	Load

Types of Movement

1 What supplies the 'effort' when cutting with scissors?

_____

2 Label **A**, **B** and **C** on the nutcrackers.

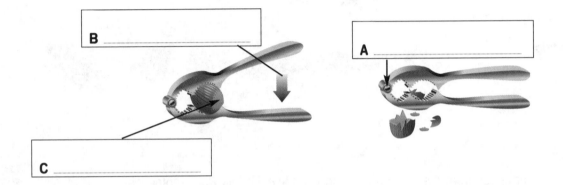

B _____

C _____

A _____

3 Choose the correct words from the options given to complete the following sentences.

multiplied   **load**   **closer**   **effort**   **fulcrum**   **force multiplier**

By altering the position of the _____, the effort can be _____ and

therefore lift a larger _____. Nutcrackers are an example of how a lever can be used

to act as a _____. In this case, the load is _____ to the fulcrum

than the _____, resulting in more force being applied.

4 Label the following diagram for a movement multiplier.

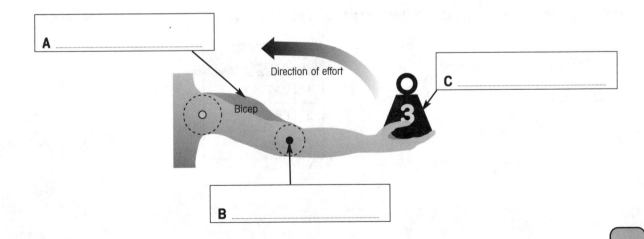

A _____

Direction of effort

C _____

Bicep

B _____

Cranks
AQA • OCR

1 What motion do cranks convert? Tick the correct option.

A Linear to oscillating

B Rotary to oscillating

C Rotary to linear

D Reciprocating to linear

2 Give an example of a child's product that uses cranks.

Cams
AQA • OCR

3 Label the following diagram showing the stages of the movement of a cam.

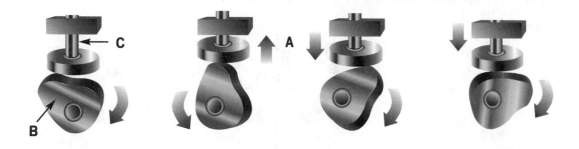

A

B

C

4 What is the purpose of a guide? Tick the correct option.

A It is a rod which moves up and down

B It converts linear motion to rotary motion

C It holds the follower in place

D It moves the follower

Types of Movement

Springs AQA • OCR

1. Match the resistance motions for springs, **A–D** with the diagrams **1–4**. Enter the appropriate number in the boxes provided.

   A Resists twisting ⬭

   B Resists compression ⬭

   C Resists extension ⬭

   D Resists radial movement ⬭

   1

   2

   3

   4

Linkages
AQA • OCR

2. Name the types of linkage systems shown in the diagrams **A–C**.

   A ....

   B ....

   C ....

Gears
AQA • OCR

3. List five products that need gears to make them move.

   a) ....

   b) ....

   c) ....

   d) ....

   e) ....

Chain and Sprocket AQA • OCR

1 What uses a chain and sprocket? Tick the correct option.

A Car ◯   **B** Tricycle ◯   **C** Crane ◯   **D** Bicycle ◯

Pulleys AQA • OCR

2 Are the following statements about pulleys **true** or **false**?

a) Used to control how fast something turns

b) Acts as a lever to transfer one motion to another

c) Used to make lifting easier

d) Used to resist radial movement

e) Can be found in cassette recorders

3 Look at the diagram of a pulley and then answer the questions that follow.

a) With a twist in the belt (pulley), what happens to wheels no. 1 and no. 2?

b) What direction is wheel no. 2 turning in?

c) What is Label **B** pointing to?

Mechanisms

1 a) What is happening in the picture below?

....

b) Give two reasons why you should 'score' with a craft knife.

i) ....   **ii)** ....

Mechanisms   AQA • OCR

2 a) What type of mechanism is illustrated in the picture below? ....

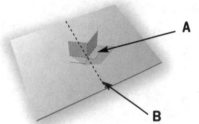

b) Fill in labels **A** and **B** on the diagram.

A ....   **B** ....

3 a) What type of mechanism is illustrated in the picture below?

....

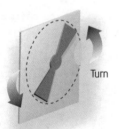

Turn

b) What component could be used to enable this mechanism to be turned by hand?

....

Mechanisms (cont.)　　AQA • OCR

1 What type of mechanism is illustrated in the following picture? Tick the correct option.

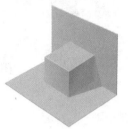

- **A** Sliding mechanism ◯
- **B** Layer mechanism ◯
- **C** Incised mechanism ◯
- **D** Rotary mechanism ◯

2 Fill in the missing labels on the following diagram.

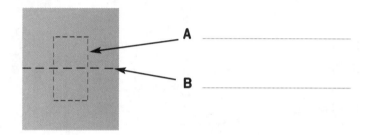

A ....

B ....

3 Choose the correct words from the options given to complete the following sentences.

incised　　　**different**　　　**3D**　　　**background**　　　**images**

A layer mechanism is similar to an .... technique, but the projected sections of

card, which project ...., are made separately to the main piece of card. This also

enables you to put images on at .... levels to the ....,

creating a layered .... image.

4 Which of the following describe a sliding mechanism? Tick the correct options.

- **A** Images on different levels to the card background ◯
- **B** The lines should be parallel and the fold line should be in the centre ◯
- **C** The mechanism projects the picture out when the card is open ◯
- **D** You move the image by pulling the end of the strip of card ◯
- **E** The image moves in one single line ◯

ICT Software

Applications of ICT

1 Name four computer system and peripheral packages available for ICT.

a) ....   b) ....

c) ....   d) ....

Word Processing Packages

2 What is it called when letters can be personalised from a database? Tick the correct option.

A Desktop publishing ☐

B Spreadsheet ☐

C Text formatting ☐

D Mail merge ☐

Spreadsheets

3 Spreadsheets enable you to put information onto a grid. What are the sections within the grid called? Tick the correct option.

A Elements ☐

B Units ☐

C Segments ☐

D Cells ☐

Desktop Publishing Packages

4 What is desktop publishing used to produce? Tick the correct options.

A Magazines and newspapers ☐

B Architectural drawings ☐

C Orthographic drawings ☐

D Leaflets ☐

E Company stationery ☐

Graphics Packages

1 a) What are art packages used for?

....

....

b) Name two art packages.

i) ....

ii) ....

2 What do drawing packages now often contain?

....

....

3 Are the following statements about Computer Aided Design (CAD) **true** or **false**?

a) It is a sophisticated drawing package.   ....

b) In industry, the most popular system is ProDesktop.   ....

c) It can be used to produce detailed 3D drawings.   ....

d) ProDesktop is one of the most popular systems used in schools. ....

e) Architects can't use it.   ....

4 Fill in the missing words to complete the following sentences.

Bitmap graphics are composed of ...., each of which contains specific

.... information.

Vector graphics consist of points, lines and ...., which can form

.... objects.

CAD and CAM Systems

CAD Systems

1 Choose the correct words from the options given to complete the following sentences.

measured **designers** **CAD** **drawing** **2D**

Computer Aided Design or .... is a .... package used by

.... and architects to create .... and 3D reality drawings.

CAD can also produce accurately .... drawings for manufacture.

2 Which of the following statements about CAD systems are true? Tick the correct options.

A It can sketch ideas. ◯

B It is easy to change the scale of the drawing. ◯

C It is easier for a designer to produce an idea using CAD than by hand. ◯

D It can produce a very realistic idea. ◯

E It is quicker and more accurate to draw by hand than on CAD. ◯

3 Are the following statements about CAD software **true** or **false**?

a) It can do mail merge. ....

b) It can produce orthographic 2D drawings. ....

c) It can produce 3D virtual reality models. ....

d) It can produce a wide range of symbols and dimensions to
easily place onto your drawing. ....

e) It can plot and cut out shapes. ....

Computer Aided Manufacture

4 Choose the correct words from the options given to complete the following sentences.

products **CAD** **components** **computers**

.... that run the manufacture of .... are sent instructions via

.... to make the .... of a product.

CAD and CAM Systems

CAM Cutters

1 What can a CAM cutter produce?

....

2 Are the following statements about CAM cutters **true** or **false**?

a) It can work by using a blade for cutting out.   ....

b) It can produce detailed pictures in 3D.   ....

c) The backing can be peeled off the vinyl.   ....

d) It can plot and cut out using coordinates from a computer. ....

e) It can produce digital images.   ....

Advantages of Using CAM

3 List four advantages of using CAM.

a) ....

b) ....

c) ....

d) ....

4 **a)** What type of CAM does the picture show?

....

b) Under what circumstances should this type of CAM be used?

....

ICT Applications

The Internet

1 What is the name of the most common feature of the internet which connects you with websites and the email system?

    A   Internet explorer ◯   **B**   World Wide Web ◯

    C   HTML ◯   **D**   ISDN ◯

2 **a)**   What does HTML stand for?

....

    b)   What is HTML?

....

3 What does surfing the internet mean?

....

....

4 Name two search engines.

    a) ....   **b)** ....

Computer Input Devices

5 Which of the following are input devices for computer systems? Tick the correct options.

    A   Bar code ◯   **B**   Laser printer ◯

    C   Digital camera ◯   **D**   Scanner ◯

    E   Plotter ◯

6 What is a graphics tablet?

....

....

7 What are concept keyboards commonly used for?

....

Computer Output Devices

1 a) What is an output device?

_____

_____

b) Name one output device that is more expensive to use than an ink-jet printer.

_____

2 The table contains the names of three types of printers.

Match statements **A, B,** and **C** with the printers **1–3** in the table.
Enter the appropriate number in the boxes provided.

	Printers
1	Ink-jet
2	Plotter
3	Laser

A Produces high quality prints, but can be expensive to use ◯

B Prints A3 paper and bigger paper sizes ◯

C Quality and speed levels are a drawback ◯

3 What is mainly used in conjunction with CAD and CAM? Tick the correct option.

A Plotters ◯

B Laser printers ◯

C Ink-jet printers ◯

Digital Media and New Technology

4 The table contains the names of three types of technology.

Match descriptions **A, B** and **C** with the terms **1–3** in the table.
Enter the appropriate number in the boxes provided.

	Technology
1	Bluetooth®
2	EPOS
3	RFID

A Identification tags that can be put on products, animals and passports ◯

B Uses radio technology to exchange data over short distances from mobile devices ◯

C Chip and pin system ◯

Safety Hazards and Control

Safety Hazards

1 When designing a toy, give one example of a safety hazard that needs to be taken into consideration.

....

Standards

2 What do the following symbols represent?

a) ....

Asbestos kills: Protect yourself!
You are more at risk than you think

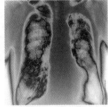

b) ....

Safety Symbols

3 Complete the following table to show what colours the symbols are and what level of warnings they give.

Symbols	Colour of Symbol	Warning
First aid post	a)	b) ....
No smoking	c)	d) ....
CAUTION ATTENTION WET FLOOR PLANCHER MOUILLÉ	e)	f) ....

© Letts and Lonsdale

Quality Control

1 What is a quality control check? Tick the correct options.

   A   Tests carried out on size and weight, etc. ◯

   B   A deadline check to make sure products are released on time ◯

   C   Checks carried out on a product as it is being made ◯

   D   Making sure a product meets a specific standard ◯

   E   A check on all the machinery used to manufacture a product ◯

2 Name three checks you could make on an injection-moulded bottle top.

Outside diameter

a) ....

b) ....

c) ....

3 What type of test does the following diagram show?

....

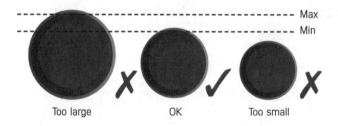

Max
Min

Too large   OK   Too small

4 In the production of a product, when can a quality control test take place? Tick the correct option.

   A   In the first stages of manufacture ◯

   B   In the final stages of manufacture ◯

   C   When the finishes are being applied ◯

   D   Anytime in the manufacturing process ◯

   E   Just before the product is transported to the shops ◯

Safety Hazards and Control

Quality Control of Printed Products

1 a) Name three ways of checking a printed product.

i) .... ii) .... iii) ....

b) What does **A** represent on the colour bar?

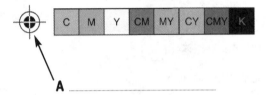

Colour Bar

A ....

Quality Assurance

2 Choose the correct words from the options given to complete the following sentences.

products   **assurance**   **standard**   **equipment**   **staff**
consistency   **manufacture**

Quality .... checks the systems that make the ...., before,

during and after .... Quality assurance ensures that .... is

achieved and that the product is of a required .... Factors such as

................................., materials, processes and .... training need to be

constantly monitored.

Non Destructive / Destructive Testing

3 a) What type of test is this picture demonstrating?

....

b) Why is this type of testing carried out?

....

....

Safety Hazards and Control

Questions for Quality Assurance

Explain why you need a customer survey in quality assurance.

....

....

....

2 You are asked to assess the quality of a new car. Suggest three questions that you could ask for each of the categories below. The first example has been done for you.

a) Design

   i) Does the design have visual appeal?

   ii) ....

   iii) ....

b) Manufacture

   i) ....

   ii) ....

   iii) ....

c) Performance

   i) ....

   ii) ....

   iii) ....

d) Customer views

   i) ....

   ii) ....

   iii) ....

© Letts and Lonsdale

Revision Guide Reference: Page 83   73

Exam-style Questions

For questions **1–10**, choose answer **A, B, C** or **D** and put a 'X' in the box for the answer you have chosen.

1 What does this symbol stand for?

A   It's raining ☐

B   Shelter ☐

C   Keep Dry ☐

D   Wet Area ☐

(1 mark)

2 What does CAM stand for?

A   Centre of Aided Manufacture ☐

B   Centre of Assurance of Manufacture ☐

C   Computer Assisted Manufacture ☐

D   Computer Aided Manufacture ☐

(1 mark)

3 What does 'biodegradable' mean?

A   Waste naturally rots in the environment ☐

B   Waste on a landfill site is reusable ☐

C   Waste cannot naturally decompose ☐

D   Waste cannot be put into recycle bins ☐

(1 mark)

4 What is one of the uses of a bar code?

A   To show what materials shop products are made from ☐

B   To keep track of stock in a business ☐

C   To tell you whether products are recyclable ☐

D   To show how much money a company is making ☐

(1 mark)

5 What is a 'target market'?

   A How a product is marketed ◯

   B Who a product is being designed for ◯

   C The method of advertising a product ◯

   D A marketing report ◯ *(1 mark)*

6 The diagram below shows a printing method.

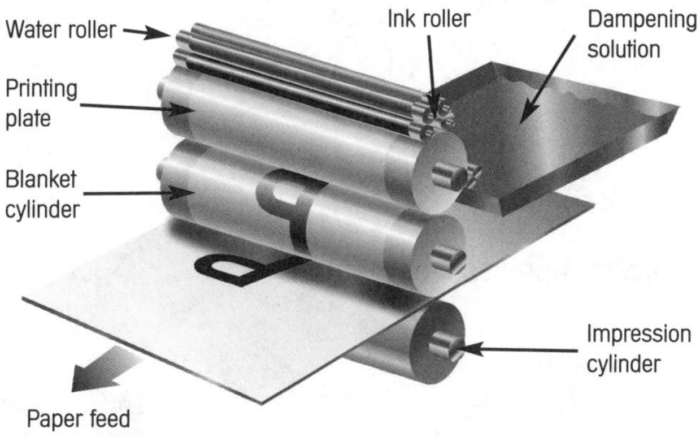

Water roller → | Ink roller | Dampening solution

Printing plate

Blanket cylinder

Impression cylinder

Paper feed

The name of the printing method is:

   A Gravure ◯

   B Offset lithography ◯

   C Letterpress ◯

   D Flexography ◯ *(1 mark)*

7 What is 'anthropometrics'?

   A Measurements of a product ◯

   B The effects the environment has on the human form ◯

   C Standard data for the human body ◯

   D Movements of the human body ◯ *(1 mark)*

8 What is 'slab bracketed'?

    A The stem of a letter

    B A type of serif on a letter

    C The bar on a letter

    D A curve on a letter   *(1 mark)*

9 What is 'microencapsulation'?

    A A document that has a high gloss finish

    B A laminated document

    C Captures scent in tiny bubbles

    D A sticker printed from microscopic dots   *(1 mark)*

10 The diagram shows the manufacturing process for a bottle.

Screw drive   Plastic   Air

Split mould

Air

Mould closes

What is the name of this process?

    A Injection moulding

    B Compression moulding

    C Vacuum forming

    D Blow moulding   *(1 mark)*

Total: 10 marks

Section B

11 In the space below, draw the Mobius Loop symbol. *(1 mark)*

12 What does the Mobius Loop symbol represent?

_____ *(1 mark)*

13 Decide whether each of the following statements are **true** or **false**.

a) Exploded drawings are perspective sketch views of the final product. **TRUE / FALSE**

b) Working drawings include specifications for materials. **TRUE / FALSE**

c) Dimensioning is done in centimetres. **TRUE / FALSE**

d) Colour contrast is when two colours do not match. **TRUE / FALSE**

e) Batch production is the production of a prototype. **TRUE / FALSE**

f) The Environment Agency licenses and regulates landfill sites. **TRUE / FALSE** *(6 marks)*

Total: 8 marks

Exam-style Questions

14 The table below shows some tools and equipment.

Complete the table by giving the missing names and the uses of each piece of equipment.

Tools / Equipment	Name	Use
	Ellipse template	
		Helps to draw an arc and can be adjusted to the right angle.
	Pair of compasses	
	Scale ruler	

(4 marks)

Total: 4 marks

15 Explain what the following words mean.

a) **Aesthetics**

....

....

.... *(2 marks)*

b) **A Development**

....

....

.... *(2 marks)*

c) **Corporate Identity**

....

....

.... *(2 marks)*

d) **Planometric**

....

....

.... *(2 marks)*

e) **Encapsulation**

....

....

.... *(2 marks)*

f) **Durability**

....

....

.... *(2 marks)*

Total: 12 marks

Exam-style Questions

16 A manufacturer wants to develop a smoothie drink.

a) What type of packaging would be suitable for this purpose?

.... *(1 mark)*

b) Explain why you have chosen this packaging.

....

.... *(3 marks)*

c) Identify three specification points for the design of this packaging.

i) ....

....

ii) ....

....

iii) ....

.... *(3 marks)*

d) Name the material and the manufacturing process for your chosen packaging.

Material: ....

Manufacturing process: .... *(2 marks)*

e) Use this page to produce sketches (minimum of 3 ideas) for a name, logo and slogan for your new smoothie design. Use annotations where necessary.

(6 marks)

f) Choose one of your initial ideas and develop it in two different ways:

Development 1

Development 2

(4 marks)

g) Draw a final presentation drawing of your logo onto your chosen packaging. Use an appropriate drawing method to present it.

(4 marks)

17 List six pieces of important information that would appear on the label for your smoothie. Give a reason why each of those items are important.

Important information	Reason
1	
2	
3	
4	
5	
6	

(6 marks)

Total: 29 marks

18 Complete the following flow chart with the next two stages of screen printing:

1. The screen is made of a wooden frame. Nylon fabric is cut, stretched and stapled to the frame.

2. _____

3. _____

(2 marks)

19 Name two products screen printing produces.

_____

_____ *(2 marks)*

20 What type of manufacturing production would the above items be produced at? Tick the correct option.

    A Continuous production ◯   **B** One-off production ◯

    C Mass production ◯   **D** Batch Production ◯

    E Just in time production ◯   *(1 mark)*

Total: 5 marks

Exam-style Questions

21 The picture is of an MP3 player.

a) Why would an MP3 player be developed as an idea on a 3D CAD programme?

....

.... *(2 marks)*

b) What type of material would be best for modelling a new idea for an MP3 player? Tick the correct option.

A Plasticine ⬭   **B** Balsa wood ⬭

C Styrofoam™ ⬭   **D** Wood ⬭

E Acrylic ⬭   *(1 mark)*

c) Give three reasons for choosing that material.

i) ....

ii) ....

iii) .... *(3 marks)*

d) Give six design specification details that need to be considered when you are producing ideas for your MP3 player.

....

....

....

....

....

....

(6 marks)

22 Use the design specification to produce two ideas. Annotate and colour your ideas.

Design Idea 1.

Design Idea 2.

(6 marks)

23 Develop one of your ideas and annotate your sketch.

(6 marks)

24 **a)** Design a logo for your MP3 Company, called **'Solar'.** Use the area below to produce a few ideas and annotate them.

(6 marks)

b) Draw the final idea for your logo and write a slogan to go with it.

Final Idea

(4 marks)

Slogan ....

c) What methods could you use to advertise your new MP3 Player? (Give 4 examples.)

(4 marks)

25 Draw your final idea of your MP3 player, which includes your logo.

(4 marks)

26 a) Now draw your design again, but show how it could be adapted so that a blind person could read the logo.

(4 marks)

b) What method have you used to produce the logo to help a blind person to recognise the company name?

_____ *(1 mark)*

27 Below are two vanishing points and the 'horizon line'. Draw your final design for your MP3 player as a two point perspective and render. You should use a grid to help you.

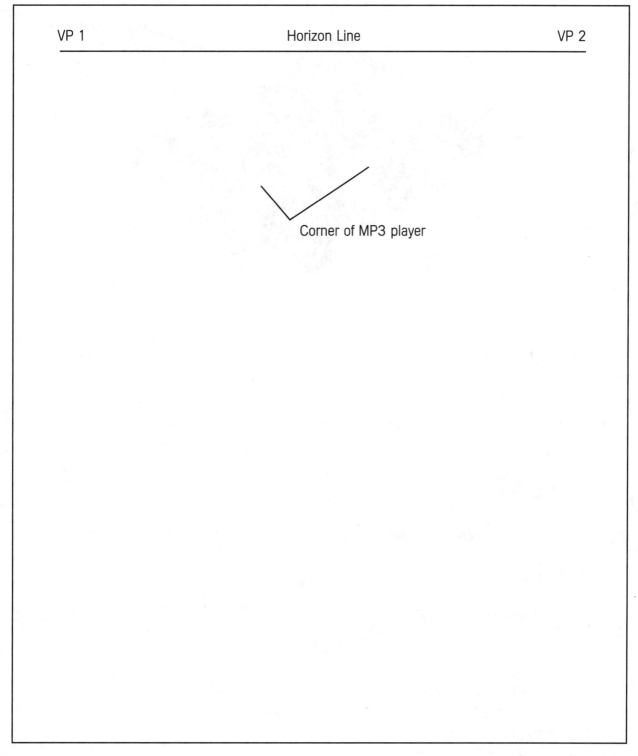

VP 1   Horizon Line   VP 2

Corner of MP3 player

(3 marks)

Total: 50 marks

Exam-style Questions

Section H

28 This question is about packaging, materials and components. Below is a picture of some drawing pins in their packaging.

Figure 01

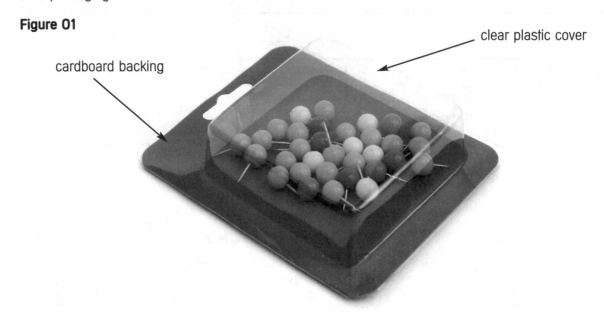

cardboard backing

clear plastic cover

a) What is the packaging called?

.... *(1 mark)*

b) Give two advantages of this type of packaging.

....

.... *(4 marks)*

29 Which part of the packaging in **Figure 01** is...

a) environmentally friendly? ....

b) not environmentally friendly? .... *(2 marks)*

30 Use sketches to show how the clear transparent cover is attached to the cardboard backing.

(4 marks)

31 a) Signs, symbols and pictograms are sometimes used on packaging instead of written instructions. Explain why.

....

....

....

.... *(1 mark)*

b) What is the meaning of the following symbol on packaging?

C E .... *(1 mark)*

32 a) What does the following symbol stand for?

.... *(2 marks)*

b) Suggest why the colours would be appropriate on this symbol.

.... *(2 marks)*

Total: 17 marks

Section I

33 Complete the table below by giving the description of each special printing effect.

One example has been done for you:

Printing Effect	Description
Metallic finish	Metallic foil, with a shiny finish, that is separately attached to the surface of paper or cardboard.
Scratch and sniff	
UV varnishing	
Embossed image	
Holographic image	

(4 marks)

34 Other than leaflets, name six ways that you can advertise a product.

a) ....

b) ....

c) ....

d) ....

e) ....

f) .... *(6 marks)*

35 a) Name two common methods of printing a batch of leaflets.

1. .... **2.** .... *(2 marks)*

b) Which of the above two methods can be used to print using a four-colour process?

.... *(1 mark)*

c) What is the last colour to be printed in this process, and why?

....

.... *(1 mark)*

36 What is a POS display and what are the advantages of using them?

....

....

....

....

....

.... *(2 marks)*

Total: 16 marks